A MIDSUMMER NIGHT'S DREAM

'True love is never easy,' says Lysander. The four young Athenians in this story – Lysander, Demetrius, Hermia, and Helena – find this out. And so, looking for answers to their difficulties, they run away to the forest outside Athens.

But Shakespeare's forest is a place where wildly impossible things happen ... The young people chase each other around the forest, but who is in love with whom, and why does love change so quickly? And they are not the only people in the forest that night. A group of workmen from the city are meeting to rehearse their play for the Duke of Athens. What extraordinary thing happens to one of the workmen? Why do his friends run from him in fear?

Because on this midsummer night, there are also fairies in the forest, spirits of the night, unseen by human eyes. They are everywhere – watching, laughing, singing, dancing, arguing. Where there are fairies, there is magic. And where there is magic, anything can happen ...

Or perhaps everything that happens is just a dream – a wonderful, midsummer night's dream ...

A Midsummer Night's Dream
Stage 3 (1000 headwords)

Series Editor: Jennifer Bassett
Founder Editor: Tricia Hedge
Activities Editors: Jennifer Bassett and Christine Lindop

RETOLD BY R. J. CORRALL

William Shakespeare's
A Midsummer
Night's Dream

Illustrated by
Fausto Bianchi

OXFORD UNIVERSITY PRESS

OXFORD

UNIVERSITY PRESS

Great Clarendon Street, Oxford, OX2 6DP, United Kingdom

Oxford University Press is a department of the University of Oxford.
It furthers the University's objective of excellence in research, scholarship,
and education by publishing worldwide. Oxford is a registered trade
mark of Oxford University Press in the UK and in certain other countries

ISBN: 978 0 19 478613 3

A complete recording of this Bookworms edition of
A Midsummer Night's Dream is available.

Printed in China

Word count (main text): 11,167

For more information on the Oxford Bookworms Library,
visit www.oup.com/elt/gradedreaders

ACKNOWLEDGEMENTS

Illustrations by: Fausto Bianchi/Beehive Illustration

CONTENTS

STORY INTRODUCTION   i

PEOPLE IN THIS STORY   viii

1 Young love   1

2 The actors   8

3 The forest   13

4 Magic in the eyes   19

5 The head of an ass   24

6 Mistakes and misunderstandings   30

7 True love returns   40

8 The play in the palace   50

GLOSSARY   59

ACTIVITIES: Before Reading   61

ACTIVITIES: While Reading   62

ACTIVITIES: After Reading   64

ABOUT WILLIAM SHAKESPEARE   68

ABOUT THE BOOKWORMS LIBRARY   70

PEOPLE IN THIS STORY

THE ATHENIANS

Theseus, *Duke of Athens*

Hippolyta, *soon to become Theseus's wife and Duchess of Athens*

Egeus, *an Athenian lord*

Hermia, *Egeus's daughter, in love with Lysander*

Lysander, *in love with Hermia*

Demetrius, *in love with Hermia*

Helena, *in love with Demetrius*

THE ACTORS

Peter Quince, *who reads the Prologue*

Nick Bottom, *who plays Pyramus*

Francis Flute, *who plays Thisbe*

Tom Snout, *who plays Wall*

Snug, *who plays Lion*

Robin Starveling, *who plays Moonshine*

THE FAIRIES

Oberon, *the fairy King*

Titania, *the fairy Queen*

Puck, *fairy servant to Oberon*

Cobweb
Peaseblossom } *fairy servants to Titania*

CHAPTER 1

Young love

Athens, on a summer night. The air is soft and warm. In the sky the moon shines, throwing its bright silvery light over the old city and the dark forest beyond. There are faces at a window in the great palace on top of the hill. It is Theseus, Duke of Athens, and the beautiful Hippolyta, looking up at the moon...

'Hippolyta, my love,' said the Duke, 'our wedding day comes closer. In four happy days there will be a new moon.' He took Hippolyta's hand and pulled her towards him. 'But how slow this old moon is!' He sighed. 'Why can't it hurry away and bring our wedding day faster.' He kissed Hippolyta's hand, and she laughed.

'Four days will quickly end in nights,' she said softly, 'and four nights will quickly pass in dreams. And then the new moon will shine on our celebrations.'

Theseus smiled. 'And they will be the finest celebrations ever seen in Athens,' he said. 'We will have happiness and smiling faces, and all the young people of Athens singing and dancing. There will be no sadness at our wedding!'

At the other end of the long palace room there was a

sudden noise. Voices were heard outside the room, and a servant opened the great doors. Theseus and Hippolyta turned to look. Four people entered. An older man, a young and beautiful woman, and two young men – all looking angry and unhappy.

'My Lord Theseus,' said the older man. He bowed deeply.

'Well, Egeus,' Theseus said. 'What's the news with you?'

'It's my daughter Hermia,' Egeus said. He spoke in a hard, angry voice. 'She will not obey me, my Lord. I have chosen a husband for her – Demetrius.' He looked at the young man on his right, who stepped forward and bowed to the Duke. 'But Hermia refuses to marry him because she says she is in love with Lysander!'

At this, the other young man now stepped forward and bowed. Egeus stared at him angrily.

'Lysander has stolen my daughter's heart, given her presents, sung under her window in the moonlight . . .' said Egeus. He turned back to the Duke. 'My Lord, the laws of Athens say a daughter must obey her father. And if she will not agree to marry Demetrius, then she must die. Is that not our Athenian law, my Lord?'

Theseus sighed. He looked at Hippolyta, but she turned away, and went to the window. Then Theseus came towards Hermia, and the young woman looked up at him. There was fear in her eyes, but she held her head up bravely.

'Well, Hermia,' said the Duke. 'You surely know, dear child, that you must obey your father in these things. He made you, he gave you your life. And he can take it away. Demetrius is a good man.'

'So is Lysander,' said Hermia. Her voice was quiet, but it seemed to fill the room.

'Yes, he is,' said the Duke calmly. 'But your father wants you to marry Demetrius, so Demetrius is the better man.'

'I wish my father would try to understand,' said Hermia.

'*You* should try to understand your father,' said the Duke. His voice was cold.

There was a little silence. Hermia looked quickly up into the Duke's face, and then away again. 'I'm sorry, my Lord,' she whispered. 'I should not speak in this way to the Duke of Athens. But please, my Lord, please tell me what will happen to me if I refuse to marry Demetrius?'

'Death,' said the Duke, 'or life in a convent, where you will never see a man again and will spend your days shut away from the world behind high walls. So think carefully, Hermia. By the next new moon – which will be my wedding day – you must choose. Death, marriage with Demetrius, or life in a convent.'

Hermia held her head high, and spoke out loudly and clearly. 'I will live and die in a convent, my Lord,' she said. 'I will not give myself to this man.'

Then everybody began to speak at once.

'Don't say that, dearest Hermia!' said Demetrius. He turned to Lysander. 'Let her go, Lysander. Egeus has given her to me!'

'You have her father's love, Demetrius,' said Lysander. 'Let me have Hermia's love. Why don't you marry him?'

Egeus began to speak angrily to Lysander, but Lysander turned to the Duke. 'My Lord, I come from just as good

a family as Demetrius, I am just as good a man as he is.
And more than all this, Hermia loves me! Why doesn't
Demetrius marry Helena? For months he's been telling
her he loves her, and she, poor girl, loves him with all her
heart. Now he won't even speak to her.'

'Mmm,' said Theseus. 'I had heard about that, and had
planned to speak to Demetrius about it. But I have been
busy with other things.' He looked at Hippolyta by the

'I will not give myself to this man,' said Hermia.

window, and smiled. 'Come, Hippolyta, we are finished here. Egeus has his answer, and Hermia must obey her father. If not, it is death or the convent. She must choose.'

The moon climbs higher in the sky, and the streets of Athens are full of a soft silvery light. The night is still young, and people are coming and going in the streets. Near the palace, there is a little square, with seats under some trees. There, Lysander meets Hermia . . .

'You look so sad, my love,' said Lysander. Hermia's eyes were red from crying, and Lysander held her hands. 'True love is never easy,' he said. 'People fall in love, and problems follow – problems of family, or money, or age . . .'

Hermia sighed. 'I know,' she said. 'It's the same for so many people. So we must be patient, and strong.'

'That's right,' Lysander said. 'And now listen, Hermia. I have an aunt. She's rich, has no children, and loves me like a son. She lives some way from Athens, and there, dearest Hermia, we can marry, because there, we will be beyond the reach of Athenian law.'

'Oh, Lysander!' cried Hermia. She threw her arms around him. 'Oh, Lysander!'

Soon they had a plan. The meeting place was in the forest outside the city walls. Tomorrow night, soon after nightfall.

'I will be there, dearest Lysander!' said Hermia. 'I promise, on my life!'

They left the square and began to walk down the street to Egeus's house – and met Helena coming the other way.

Helena had been Hermia's friend since they were both young children. These days, because of her hopeless love for Demetrius, Helena always looked unhappy.

'How are you, Helena?' said Hermia brightly. 'You're looking well.'

'Oh, don't say that!' Helena said. 'I never look as good as you. And that's why Demetrius loves you, and not me. To him, your eyes are stars, your voice sweeter than a songbird's. I just wish I had your voice, your eyes, your mouth. Can't you teach me how to make him love me?'

Hermia sighed. 'I give him hard words, and he gives me love.'

'I give him sweet words, and he gives me nothing!' cried Helena.

'I hate him more and more,' said Hermia, 'but he just follows me.'

'I love him more and more,' said Helena, 'and he just hates me.' The sadness in her face was terrible to see.

'Listen,' Hermia said. 'We'll tell you our secret. After tomorrow, Demetrius will never see my face again. Lysander and I are leaving Athens.'

Helena stared, her eyes wide with surprise, as Hermia and Lysander explained their plan to escape from Athens, to find a new life, among new friends.

'Wish us luck, dear Helena,' said Hermia. 'And we wish you luck with Demetrius. I hope he soon loves you as much as you love him.'

Hermia kissed Helena goodbye, and they all went home their different ways.

Helena had much to think about. 'How happy they are!' she thought. 'Everyone in Athens thinks I'm as pretty as Hermia, but Demetrius doesn't think so. He used to love me – until he saw Hermia. I think I'll go and tell him that Hermia is running away from Athens, and then perhaps he will thank me. Perhaps he will be grateful . . . and even smile at me.'

'How happy they are!' thought Helena.

CHAPTER 2

The actors

That same evening, in a little house in Athens, six men are having a meeting – Peter Quince, Nick Bottom, Francis Flute, Tom Snout, Snug, and Robin Starveling. They are all workmen, good honest workmen, who make and mend things with their hands – tables and chairs, shoes and shirts, pots and pans. They are talking excitedly. The Duke's wedding is in four days' time, and they have a grand plan to entertain the wedding guests . . .

'Is everybody here?' said Peter Quince.

The six men were all sitting round a big wooden table. Nobody answered Peter Quince at first because they were all too busy talking. Then Nick Bottom looked up.

'You need to call out the names, one after t'other,' he said loudly. Nick Bottom was a large man, who liked talking and usually had a lot to say.

'Yes, all right, Bottom,' said Quince, crossly. He stood up and banged his hand on the table. Everybody stopped talking and looked at him.

Quince held up a piece of paper. 'Here are the names,' he said importantly. 'These men are chosen – from all

Athens – to act in our play before the Duke and Duchess on their wedding day.'

Everybody watched Peter Quince, waiting.

'You need to tell us about the play, Peter,' said Bottom loudly. 'Then read the names of the actors, and then—'

'The play is . . .' began Quince quickly. He tried to make his voice louder than Bottom's. 'The play is *The sad and funny story of the cruel death of Pyramus and Thisbe.*'

'Oh, that's a very good play,' said Bottom. 'And now the names, Peter Quince, the names!'

'You, Nick Bottom,' said Quince, 'will play Pyramus – a lover who kills himself, very beautifully, for love.'

'Aha!' said Bottom. 'I'll make the audience cry! They'll cry for hours at my death – there'll be a storm of crying! I'll be so sad . . . But I can do strong, cruel kings too, you know. I'm very good at cruel kings.'

He stood up and began to speak some lines from an old play in a deep, strong voice.

Peter Quince waited patiently. No one could stop Bottom when he started talking.

'But I can play a good lover too,' said Bottom, sitting down at last. 'I shall play a gentle, sad lover.'

Quince picked up his piece of paper again. 'Francis Flute,' he said. 'You must play Thisbe.'

'What's Thisbe? A brave fighter?' said Flute.

'It's the lady that Pyramus loves,' Quince said.

'Oh no,' said Flute. 'I don't want to play a woman! I have a beard coming.' Francis Flute was a small thin man, with not a single hair on his face.

'Never mind about that!' said Quince. 'You can cover your face, and speak in a little high voice.'

'If I can hide my face, let me play Thisbe too,' Bottom said. 'I can do all the voices – listen! Thisbe, Thisbe!' he shouted in a deep voice. Then he changed to his Thisbe voice, which was much higher, but just as loud. 'Ah, Pyramus, my lover dear.'

'No, no,' said Peter Quince. He shook his finger at Bottom. 'You must play Pyramus; and Flute, you Thisbe.'

'Oh well, go on, then,' said Bottom.

'Robin Starveling?' said Quince.

'Here, Peter Quince,' said a tall, very thin man.

'You must play Thisbe's mother. Tom Snout?'

'Here, Peter Quince,' said Snout.

'You're playing Pyramus's father,' said Quince. 'I'm playing Thisbe's father, and Snug, you're the lion. And there's our play.'

Snug looked worried. 'Can you give me the lion's words now? I'm slow at learnin' things.'

'You don't need words,' Quince said kindly. 'You only have to roar.'

'Let me play the lion too,' said Bottom, full of excitement. 'I'll roar like twenty lions. The Duke will say, "Let's hear that lion roar again!" They'll love it!'

He got up and began to jump around, pretending to be a lion, moving his head from side to side. Suddenly, he gave a very loud roar. Snug jumped in his chair, and Tom Snout put his hands over his ears.

'Very good,' said Quince. 'But if you roar like that,

'I'll roar like twenty lions,' said Nick Bottom.

you'll frighten the Duchess and all the ladies to death. Then they'll send us to our deaths too.'

'Yes, that'll be the end of all of us,' said Robin Starveling.

'Ah,' said Bottom. 'Yes, you're right. Well, I'll roar softly then. I'll roar you as softly and gently as a baby bird.'

Quince sighed. 'No, you won't,' he said. 'You'll play Pyramus, Bottom. Pyramus is a good man, a fine man – you couldn't meet a nicer man than Pyramus anywhere. So you must play Pyramus.'

'Well, I'll do it, then.' Bottom thought for a minute. 'What beard should I play it in?'

'You can wear what beard you like,' said Quince.

'What about a light yellow beard?' said Bottom. 'Or maybe a dark yellow. Perhaps a red beard would be better – or that French golden colour . . .'

'Let's not worry about the beard!' said Quince. 'Here, everyone, are the words you must learn.' He gave a paper to everyone except Snug. 'Learn your words by tomorrow night, and meet me in the palace forest, at the Duke's oak tree. We'll rehearse there by moonlight. If we meet in the city, everyone will know about our plans. So, make sure you come to the forest!'

'We'll be there,' said Bottom. 'Make sure you know your words, everyone! Work hard!'

The six actors said goodnight, and went out into the warm Athens night.

CHAPTER 3

The forest

The forest beyond the city of Athens is a dark and mysterious place. If you walk there at night, you may see lights moving among the trees, hear voices singing and music playing. But you do not often see them, these spirits of the night. They are fairies, and they live and move in a different air from us. Tonight, both the Fairy Queen and the Fairy King are in the forest, but all is not well between them . . .

At the foot of a little hill, a fairy lay on his back in the grass, hands behind his head, enjoying the warm summer night. This was Puck, a servant to Oberon, the Fairy King.

Puck heard something in the trees behind him, and turned his head to look. A pretty young fairy flew down from the trees and landed on the grass.

'And where are you going?' Puck called out lazily.

The fairy looked at him, surprised. 'Titania, our Fairy Queen, comes here tonight,' she said. 'I must get all the flowers ready for her.'

'What!' Puck sat up quickly. 'But the King is coming here tonight as well. He's furious with the Queen because she won't let him take her new servant boy.'

'Yes, I know. It's that lovely little boy that the Queen brought back from India,' the fairy said. 'He's her favourite servant at the moment – she plays with him all day. The boy's mother was the Queen's friend in India, but the mother died when the boy was born.'

'Well, Oberon wants the boy, and the Queen won't let him go,' said Puck. 'They argue about it night and day.'

The fairy was staring closely at Puck.

'You're Puck, aren't you?' she said. 'That mischievous spirit who's always making trouble. You frighten young women in the villages, you stop their milk from turning into butter, and you make people lose their way in the night.'

Puck laughed. It was all true. He loved to go around at night, making trouble – and making Oberon laugh.

There are noises in the forest, and green lights come dancing through the trees. Oberon arrives, with his fairy servants. Then there are more lights – white ones, from the other side of the forest, and Titania and her servants appear. The King and Queen stop when they see each other, and a little cold wind blows through the tops of the trees. Puck and the fairy disappear behind a tree . . .

'Ah, Titania!' said Oberon, with a most unpleasant smile. 'What an unwelcome meeting!'

'My jealous husband!' said Titania. She turned her back on Oberon. 'Come, fairies, let's go. I don't want to be near him.'

'Not so fast!' said Oberon, taking Titania's arm. 'I am your husband, and you should do what I say.'

Titania pushed Oberon's hand from her arm. 'Then I am your wife, and you should love only me,' she said angrily. 'But I know all about your journeys out of Fairyland to see your lovely, loving Phillida – playing music to her, singing love songs. And why are you here now? Because Hippolyta – who you love – is marrying Theseus!'

'Don't talk about Hippolyta like that!' cried Oberon. 'I know all about you and Theseus. You are always stealing him away from the women he loves!'

Titania laughed. 'These are lies made by your jealousy! Oberon, since early summer, every time my fairies and I have met to dance for the wind, you have come and argued with us. Now the wind has grown angry, and brought terrible rains down on the land, filling the rivers, destroying the farmer's fields. No one knows if it is winter, spring, summer, or autumn. There is ice on the flowers, and summer plants grow in the snow. All this because of us.'

Oberon moved closer to Titania, and spoke softly. 'Then you must make things better! Why do you want to fight your loving Oberon? All I ask is that little boy for my servant.'

'I will not give you that child for all of Fairyland,' said Titania. She turned away and sat on the low branch of a tree. 'His mother was my friend – and that is why I keep him with me, and why I will not let him go.'

'How long will you stay in the forest?' Oberon asked.

There were little golden yellow flowers in the Queen's long black hair. She took a flower from her hair and threw it to Oberon. He caught it in his hand.

'Perhaps until after Theseus's wedding day,' said Titania.

'Why don't you come and dance with us, and watch our moonlight celebrations?'

'Give me that boy, and I will,' said Oberon.

'No, not for all your Fairyland.' Titania turned away. 'Come, fairies, let's go. We will go on arguing if I stay.'

'Why don't you come and dance with us?' said Titania.

Titania and her fairies flew away into the forest, their white lights dancing through the trees. Oberon stared after her. 'I'll make trouble for her for this,' he said to himself. He turned to Puck, who had come out from behind his tree.

'Come here, Puck,' said Oberon. He put his arm around Puck's shoulders. 'I showed you once, you remember, a little purple flower. It has a magic juice. When you put the juice on the eyes of a man or woman as they sleep, it makes them fall in love with the next thing they see. Fetch me that magic flower, Puck, and do it quickly.'

'I'll be round the world and back in forty minutes!' said Puck, and he disappeared into the tree tops.

Oberon smiled to himself. He would put some of this magic juice in Titania's eyes while she was sleeping. Then when she woke up, she would fall in love with the next thing she saw – lion or dog or horse. 'I can use another flower juice to take the magic away,' he said to himself. 'But before I do, I'll make her give me her little servant boy.'

There are voices in the forest, but these are the voices of humans – a man, angry, and a woman, crying – and they are coming closer. Humans cannot see fairies, so Oberon sits on the branch of a tree, to watch and to listen . . .

Demetrius ran to the foot of the little hill, followed closely by Helena. He turned around angrily towards her.

'I don't love you,' he shouted, 'so don't follow me! Where are Lysander and Hermia? You told me they'd run away into this forest! Now go away, and stop following me.'

Helena had run after Demetrius all the way from Athens, and now she fell to the ground and put her head on his feet. 'I don't care if you don't love me, Demetrius. But please let me go with you.'

Demetrius shook her from his feet. 'You make me sick! I hope wild animals come and take you away!'

'How can you be so unkind?' said Helena, as Demetrius turned and left. 'Go on, then – run, and I'll follow. I love you so much, I don't care if you kill me.' She ran after Demetrius into the trees.

Oberon watched her go. 'Poor girl,' he said.

A shadow passed across the moon, and Puck flew down to the ground. He opened his hand, and showed Oberon some small purple flowers.

'Give them to me, Puck,' said Oberon. 'I know a place in the forest where the sweetest wild flowers grow. Titania sleeps there some of the night. I shall find her and put the juice of the flower on her eyes.' He laughed to himself, and gave one of the flowers back to Puck. 'You take some of the juice too. A sweet Athenian lady in the forest is in love with a cruel young man. Put some of the juice in the man's eyes when he is sleeping. But be sure that the first thing he sees when he wakes up will be this woman. You'll know the man because of his Athenian clothes. Do it well. Then meet me before the sun comes up.'

'Yes, my Lord, at once,' said Puck.

CHAPTER 4

Magic in the eyes

In a grassy clearing in another part of the forest, white lights dance in the trees, and music plays. Wild flowers wave gently in the soft wind, and the air is sweet. Titania, the Fairy Queen, is resting here. Her fairy servants watch over her, and sing their queen to sleep . . .

Moon above us, shine so bright,
Let us sing a sweet goodnight.

Oberon, on the edge of the clearing, watched as the fairies sang Titania to sleep. When the music ended, they went away, and he came closer. One fairy servant had stayed to watch over the Queen, but when she looked up, he blew in her eyes, and at once she fell asleep. Oberon went silently up to Titania and touched her face. Then he pressed the purple flower in his hand, so that drops of juice fell onto her eyes. Small silver lights danced across the Fairy Queen's head, and Oberon sang softly:

When you wake, your eyes will change.
You'll fall in love with something strange.

'When you wake, your eyes will change,' sang Oberon.

Oberon was gone as quickly as he had come, and a moment later Lysander and Hermia walked into the clearing. Lysander looked around, worried.

'Hermia, you're tired, and I'm not sure where we are any more. Let's lie down for a bit and wait for morning.'

'I'll sleep here,' said Hermia. 'There's some nice soft

grass, just here.' She lay down on her side, made herself comfortable, and closed her eyes.

Lysander lay down next to her. 'We can both sleep here,' he said, but she pushed him away.

'No, Lysander. Go and lie over there, not near me.'

'Oh, sweetest,' he said, putting his hand on her arm. 'I only want to sleep here beside you, I promise.'

Hermia laughed, moving his hand away.

'Lysander, we're not married. We can't sleep next to each other.'

He smiled and sighed. Then he moved away from Hermia and lay down.

'I'll sleep over here then. Good night, Hermia.'

'Sleep well,' said Hermia, her eyes already closing.

The lovers slept, and a little while later Puck arrived in the clearing. He had gone all through the forest looking for a man in Athenian clothes, but found nobody. Now, stepping quietly across the grassy clearing, he saw two people sleeping on the ground.

'This must be the man from Athens that Oberon was talking about,' Puck said. 'And here's the sweet lady who he's so cruel to. Poor thing, lying on the dirty ground, afraid to go near him!'

Puck took out the purple flower, and held it over Lysander, letting its juice fall into his eyes. As silver lights moved across Lysander's face, Puck whispered:

> You will wake with love that's deep,
> Love that keeps you from your sleep.

Puck turned and hurried quickly away through the trees. But only a moment later, there were voices in that part of the forest once more, and Demetrius arrived in the clearing, followed closely by Helena. Helena was exhausted. She fell to the ground, taking Demetrius's arm and pulling on it.

'Please don't go, Demetrius!' she cried.

'Leave me alone!' he said, shaking himself free. 'I don't care what happens to you!'

He ran on, and Helena lay on the ground crying. Why had she ever thought that Demetrius could love her? Why had she followed him here? Then, through her tears, she saw Lysander lying on the grass.

'Lysander!' she cried. 'Are you all right? Are you hurt?' She shook his shoulders. 'Lysander, wake up!'

Lysander opened his eyes, saw Helena, and at once his face lit up with love. He sat up, unable to take his eyes away from her.

'Helena!' he cried. 'Helena, I'd do anything for you!' He remembered Demetrius, and looked around. 'Where's Demetrius? I'll kill him!'

'Lysander!' Helena said. 'Don't be so angry with him, just because he loves Hermia. Hermia still loves you.'

'Hermia?' said Lysander, taking Helena's hand. 'I don't care about her any more! It's you that I love, Helena.'

Helena pulled her hand away, furiously.

'Why are you making fun of me?' she shouted. 'I thought you were a good man, Lysander! How can you laugh at me like this?'

With that, Helena turned and ran away into the forest,

'Helena, I'd do anything for you!' Lysander cried.

after Demetrius. Lysander looked at Hermia, sleeping on the ground. Then he got up and followed Helena.

A little later, Hermia woke from a terrible dream.

'Lysander!' she cried, sitting up. She looked across at the ground where he had been asleep.

'Where are you?' she shouted, terrified. 'Lysander, where are you?' And she ran away into the forest.

CHAPTER 5

The head of an ass

In that same part of the forest where Titania lies sleeping, our six actors meet to rehearse in the clearing. The grass makes a fine stage for them. But one of the actors, Nick Bottom, is worried . . .

'Peter Quince,' he said. 'There's things in this play about Pyramus and Thisbe that the audience won't like. First, Pyramus kills himself with a sword, doesn't he? Well, that'll be terrifying for the ladies.'

'Oh yes,' agreed Snout. 'They won't like that at all!'

'Well, we must leave the killing out, then,' said Starveling.

'No, no, no,' said Bottom. 'I know what to do. We'll have a prologue – yes! We'll tell 'em that the swords don't hurt nobody, and Pyramus doesn't get killed at all. And even better, we'll say that I, Pyramus, am not Pyramus, but Bottom, a workman. How about that? Then there's nothing for 'em to be afraid of.'

Everybody agreed that was a good idea. Then there was another worry . . .

'Won't the ladies be afraid of the lion?' said Snout.

'Well, I'm afraid of it,' said Starveling. 'I know that!'

'So we'll need another prologue, then,' Snout said, 'to say he's not a lion.'

But Bottom had another idea. 'No. Listen,' he said. 'We must show half of Snug's face through the lion's neck. And then Snug says, "Dear ladies, please don't be afraid. I am not a lion – I am a man, and my name is Snug."'

'That's all well and good, then,' said Quince. 'But here's another thing. How will we make moonlight on the stage? Because Pyramus and Thisbe meet by moonlight, you know. How are we goin' to do that?'

'Oh, that's easy! If there's a moon on the night of our play,' said Bottom, 'we can leave a window open, and then the moon can shine in through the window.'

'Well, yes,' said Quince. 'Or now here's another idea. Someone can come in holdin' a light, and they can say "I am here to show Moonshine." Now, what do we do about the wall? Because Pyramus and Thisbe, says the story, speak through a hole in the wall.'

'Well, we can't bring in a wall,' said Snout. 'What do you say, Bottom?'

'Someone must play the Wall,' replied Bottom. 'He can hold a stone or somethin', and he can have his fingers like this, to make a hole.' Bottom put his finger and thumb together to make a circle. 'Then Pyramus and Thisbe can whisper through that hole.'

'That's all good then,' said Quince. 'Come and sit down, everyone, and rehearse your words. Bottom, you start. Then when you've said your words, go and stand behind those trees over there.'

While the actors were getting themselves into the right places, Puck came past the clearing.

'What's going on here, so near the sleeping place of our Fairy Queen?' he said. He stopped to look, and smiled. 'A play, eh? Well, I'll watch it – and be an actor too, perhaps.'

The actors were now ready. Flute was waiting in the trees, Bottom was standing in the middle of the grassy clearing, and Quince and the others sat round the edge.

'Speak, Pyramus!' said Quince in a loud whisper, and then in another loud whisper to Flute: 'Thisbe, come forward!'

Flute moved out of the trees, and Bottom, as Pyramus, began to say his words in a loud voice: 'Thisbe, Thisbe, your breath smells so sickly, like beautiful flowers!'

'Sweetly!' called Quince. 'Smells so *sweetly. Not sickly!*'

Bottom started again. 'Your breath smells so sweetly, like beautiful flowers, my dearest Thisbe dear. But listen! I hear a voice! Stay here, my love, I must go and see what it is.' He ran from the stage into the trees at the edge of the clearing.

'Er, do I speak now?' Flute asked uncomfortably.

'Yes, yes,' said Quince. 'Pyramus has only gone to see what the noise is. He'll be back in a minute.'

Flute spoke next, in a high little voice, trying to sound like a woman. 'Most lovely Pyramus, so young, so quick, so good, so bright. You're as true and strong as any horse. Yes, Pyramus, I'll meet you at Castle gate.'

'No, no, no!' said Quince. 'You mustn't say about the meeting yet. You say those words to Pyramus later. You're saying all your words at once! Say your last line again.'

'Oh,' said Flute. 'You're as true and strong as any horse.'

'Pyramus!' shouted Quince. 'Pyramus, come back onto the stage! You come back when Flute says *as any horse.*'

Bottom came out of the trees and ran back into the clearing, saying his next words, 'Thisbe, loveliest Thisbe, here I come!'

The actors stared at him, in terrified silence. Bottom now had the head of an ass, with long grey hairy ears and big brown eyes.

'Oh, Bottom!' cried Quince. 'What have you got on your head? Something terrible's happened to you. Run, men! Help!' And, shouting with fear, the men ran into the forest.

It was Puck, of course, who had given Bottom the ass's head. Now he looked on, enjoying his mischief.

Bottom stood on his own in the clearing, scratching his ass's head. 'Why have they run away?' he asked himself. 'Oh, I see, they're just playing games with me. Yes, they're trying to make a fool of me. Well, they won't frighten me away. I'll walk up and down, and sing, and then they'll know that Nick Bottom is not afraid.'

In the trees by the clearing Titania sleeps in her flowery bed. She is woken by Bottom's song, looks down to the clearing, and sees him with his ass's head. The purple flower has worked its magic, and the voice, and its singer, are wonderful to her. She sees him – and loves him at once . . .

'Oh, sing again!' Titania cried out, when Bottom finished his song. 'The sound of your voice is sweet to my ear, and every part of you is beautiful to my eye. How I love you!'

Bottom now had the head of an ass.

Bottom turned his head, and saw a beautiful woman standing behind him.

'Well, Madam,' he said, and he looked around to see if she was talking to someone else. 'This is a surprise!'

Titania had come close to Bottom now, and she touched his ass's ears gently, and kissed his head. 'Stay here with me,' she said softly. 'My fairies will be your servants. They will bring you presents, and sing to you, while you sleep on a bed of flowers.'

She turned and called two of her fairy servants, Cobweb and Peaseblossom, who flew down from the trees.

'Be kind and good to this gentleman,' said Titania. 'Feed him with the sweetest fruit from the forest, and fetch flowers to keep the moonlight from his sleeping eyes. Come, do what he wishes, and bring him to my night palace.' And together with her servants, Titania led Bottom away through the forest.

CHAPTER 6

Mistakes and misunderstandings

It is dark and quiet in the forest now, and a gentle wind blows through the trees. Oberon, the Fairy King, looks up at the stars and thinks about his Queen Titania. Then he hears his servant Puck coming through the forest . . .

'What news, my mischievous boy?' said Oberon.

Puck laughed. 'I found a group of actors in the forest, right near the Fairy Queen's bed! A simple, stupid group, who were rehearsing the play *Pyramus and Thisbe* for the Duke's wedding night. The actor who was Pyramus was the simplest and stupidest of them all, so when he was waiting behind some trees, I came up behind him . . . and did a little Puck magic. I gave him an ass's head! Seeing him like this, the others ran away, terrified. And when Titania awoke, she fell in love – with an ass!'

Oberon was very pleased with this news. 'This is better than I'd hoped!' he said, laughing. 'But have you put love-juice on the young Athenian's eyes yet?'

'Yes,' said Puck, 'and the woman was lying near him. When he wakes up, he'll see her before anything else!'

'Quick! Move away! Here he comes!' said Oberon.

Demetrius and Hermia came running through the trees, and Puck's eyes widened. 'Oh no – this is the woman I saw, but it's not the same man.'

🍁 🍁 🍁

Hermia was shouting at Demetrius. 'Lysander would never leave me while I was sleeping! You've murdered him! I know you have!'

'I haven't killed him!' said Demetrius. 'You're the one who is killing me, with your cruel words!'

'I only care about Lysander,' said Hermia. 'Where is he? Did you kill him when he was sleeping?'

'I didn't kill him,' said Demetrius, 'and he's not dead.'

'I'm going! And don't follow me!' said Hermia, and she turned and ran away into the forest. Demetrius sighed. He was exhausted from walking all night. He lay down on the ground, and was soon asleep.

🍁 🍁 🍁

'Look what you've done now, Puck!' Oberon cried angrily. 'You've put the love-juice on the wrong man's eyes! We were supposed to help that poor woman Helena. Now this woman Hermia has lost her lover – because of you!'

He thought quickly. 'Go through the forest, find Helena and bring her here, where Demetrius is sleeping. And be quick.' He took out the last purple flower, pressed the juice from it into Demetrius's eyes, and said:

Now Helena will please your eye,
And be your love, until you die.

Silver lights were just beginning to dance across
Demetrius's face when Puck arrived back.

'Helena's coming, my Lord,' he said. 'And the other
young man, who I gave the love-juice to. So now both men
will be in love with the same woman! Oh, what fools these
humans are!'

A few moments later, there were voices in the forest, and
Lysander and Helena arrived in the clearing. Oberon and
Puck stepped back into the trees, to watch and listen.

Lysander was trying to take hold of Helena's hand.
'Helena, I love you, I promise,' he said. 'Why would I
pretend to you?'

'Stop lying to me, Lysander!' said Helena. 'You love
Hermia. What about your promises to her?'

Their voices woke Demetrius, and as he sat up, the
magic of Oberon's love-juice began to work. He looked
at Helena, and his face was full of love. 'Oh, Helena!' he
cried. 'Lovely, beautiful Helena! Those eyes, those lips, that
snow-white hand!' He took Helena's hand, as she looked
at him, astonished. 'Let me kiss it!'

Helena pulled her hand away. 'Why do you want to hurt
me like this?' she cried. 'I know you both hate me. Can't you
leave it at that? Why do you have to make fun of me too?'

Lysander turned on Demetrius. 'You're being unkind,
Demetrius,' he said. 'You love Hermia. Take her, and let
me have Helena. I love her, and I'll love her until I die.'

'You can keep Hermia,' said Demetrius. 'If ever I loved
her, that love's gone. My heart is here with Helena now,
and that's where it'll stay.'

Now another angry voice was heard and Hermia came running through the trees. 'Lysander! Why did you leave me?' she shouted.

'Why would I stay with you?' Lysander said coldly. 'I was following my true love.'

'What?' cried Hermia. 'What are you talking about?'

'I came after Helena, the light of my life,' said Lysander. 'Why did you come looking for me? I don't want you any more. Can't you see that?'

Hermia fell to her knees, astonished. 'This can't be true! It can't be!'

Helena looked from Lysander to Hermia. 'So now all three of you are making fun of me! How can you do this to me, Hermia?' she cried. 'I thought we were best friends! Have you forgotten all those years when we were like sisters? And you want to destroy all that, and join with these men to make fun of me? No woman should do that to her friend!'

'I don't understand what you're talking about!' said Hermia. 'I'm not making fun of you!'

Helena's face was red and angry. 'You send Lysander to tell me that he loves me! And you tell Demetrius to call me 'beautiful'! Demetrius hates me, you know he does. Isn't that enough for you? Now you have to make fun of me too! I thought you were my friend. How can you do this to me!'

Helena turned to go, but Lysander took her hand and pulled her back. 'Helena, my love! Don't go!'

'Don't make fun of Helena like this, Lysander,' said Hermia. She put her hand on his arm, but he shook her off.

'Helena, I love you more than Lysander,' said Demetrius.

'*I'm not too little to scratch your eyes out!*' shouted Hermia.

'Then show it!' cried Lysander, taking out his sword. 'Come on, let's fight for her.'

Hermia ran up behind Lysander and threw her arms around him, holding him back.

'Get off me!' shouted Lysander, trying to free his arms. Demetrius had taken out his sword too. 'I thought you wanted to fight!' he said coldly.

'What can I do?' cried Lysander, as he tried to get free from Hermia. 'Kill her? I hate her, but I won't hurt her.'

'Hate me?' shouted Hermia, and she let go of Lysander and looked at him astonished. 'You hate me?'

'Yes,' said Lysander cruelly. 'I never want to see you again. I hate you, and I love Helena.'

Hermia looked at Helena now, her eyes full of hate. 'What happened last night? You stole my love from me!'

She ran at Helena and pushed her, and Helena fell to the ground.

'You should be ashamed of yourself!' Helena cried, as Lysander helped her stand up. 'You little wildcat!'

'Oh, it's "little" now, is it?' shouted Hermia. 'Just because you're so tall and I'm so short! Well, let me tell you, I'm not too little to scratch your eyes out!'

Hermia jumped at Helena again, reaching for her eyes, but Demetrius quickly stepped between them. He held Hermia back from Helena.

'Don't let her hurt me!' Helena said to Demetrius and Lysander. 'I'm not brave, and she's much stronger than me.'

She looked at Hermia, who was trying to pull her arms away from Demetrius's hold.

'I've always loved you, Hermia,' she said, gently. 'I've never done anything to hurt you. It's all because I love Demetrius so much. I told him you'd come here, and I thought he'd be pleased with me, but he was cruel. He told me to go away – he even said he'd kill me. I just want to go back to Athens now.'

'Go on, then!' said Hermia. 'What's stopping you?'

Helena didn't move. She looked at the ground and sighed. 'I'm still in love,' she said quietly.

'With Lysander?' Hermia shouted.

'No!' said Helena. 'With Demetrius.'

'Don't be afraid, Helena,' said Lysander, taking her hand. 'I won't let Hermia hurt you.'

'I can take care of you, Helena,' said Demetrius. 'Don't listen to Lysander.'

'My hands are free now,' said Lysander, holding up his sword. 'Let's go and see who loves Helena the most. If you're brave enough!'

'I'm not afraid to fight you!' said Demetrius.

The two men walked away into the forest, and Helena and Hermia were left alone together.

'This is all because of you,' Hermia said angrily. 'Don't try and run away!'

'I'm not staying here!' cried Helena. 'You're a better fighter than me, but my legs are longer, and I can run away!' With that, she was gone.

Hermia stood alone for a moment, then she followed Helena into the forest.

Oberon stepped out from the trees. 'Look what you've done,' he said to Puck. 'Is this more of your mischief?'

'My Lord, it was a mistake,' said Puck hurriedly. 'You told me to look for a man in Athenian clothes – and I found one. But it's been funny to watch these humans – how they argue and fight, just because of love!'

'They're looking for a place to fight,' said Oberon. 'So go, Puck, and cover the night with a black fog. Pretend to be Lysander one moment, then Demetrius the next. Make them follow you, but make sure they never see each other.'

Oberon took some small white flowers from his pocket, and gave one to Puck. 'In the end they'll fall down exhausted, and sleep. Then put the juice of this flower into Lysander's eyes. It undoes the magic of the purple flower. When they wake up, the lovers will think this night has just been a strange dream. They'll go back to Athens and live happily together.'

He looked at the white flowers in his hand, and smiled. 'While you're doing this, I'll go and ask my Queen for her Indian boy. Then I'll free her from her love for this human ass, and our lives will be peaceful again.'

Now the morning star begins to shine in the sky, and soon the golden sun will come up in the east. Oberon hurries away to find his queen, while our mischievous Puck busies himself with the work of the Fairy King. Very soon a dark fog comes down on the forest, hiding the starlit sky . . .

For some time, Puck led Demetrius and Lysander away from each other through the forest. First he used Lysander's voice, then Demetrius's voice, then Lysander's again. And every time he called, the two young Athenians ran through the forest, never finding each other, and getting more and more tired. At last, exhausted, Lysander lay down to sleep.

Puck led Demetrius and Lysander
away from each other through the forest.

Demetrius was tired of looking for Lysander too. Puck led him back to the clearing where Lysander lay. In the fog Demetrius could not see Lysander lying there. He lay down to wait for morning, and soon he too fell asleep.

Was it Puck who led the two sad young women back to that same part of the forest? Or was it the hearts of the men they loved? First came Helena. She lay down to sleep, hoping to escape from the unhappiness of that endless night. Then Hermia arrived, heartbroken and exhausted. Soon all four lovers lay asleep on the ground.

Puck waited for a while, and then stepped quietly to where Lysander lay. He took out the little white flower that Oberon had given him, and pressed it into his hand. Drops of juice from the flower fell onto Lysander's face, and silver lights danced into his eyes, as Puck spoke quietly.

> True love returns, when next you wake,
> And puts an end to all heartbreak.

'Every man will love the right woman,' said Puck, laughing, 'and all will be well.'

CHAPTER 7

True love returns

Above the clearing where the lovers sleep on the grassy ground, is Titania's night palace in the tree-tops. Here music plays all night long, and fairy servants laugh and sing. Here, on her bed of flowers, the Fairy Queen entertains her new love – Nick Bottom in an ass's head. From the shadows of the next tree, Oberon watches her . . .

'Come, my love,' said Titania, gently touching Bottom's hairy face. 'Let me put flowers round your head, and kiss your lovely big ears.'

Bottom sighed happily and lay back on the bed. 'Where's Peaseblossom?' he said.

A white light danced towards the bed. 'I'm here,' said Peaseblossom.

'Scratch my head, Peaseblossom,' said Bottom. He shut his eyes as Peaseblossom began to scratch behind his ears. 'Ah, that's good! Where's Mr Cobweb?'

'I'm here,' said Cobweb, appearing at Bottom's side.

'Ah, Mr Cobweb, my good man. Yes, would you help Madam Peaseblossom to scratch my head? Ah, good, good, that's very good!'

While the fairy servants scratched his head, Bottom put his hand on his long ass's face. 'Hmm,' he said, 'I must get my beard cut. I'm very hairy – all over my face.'

'Would you like some music, my sweet love?' asked Titania. 'Or something to eat, perhaps?'

'Hmm, an armful of sweet summer grass would be nice,' said Bottom, putting his hand on his large stomach.

Titania kissed the ass's soft nose. 'I'll ask my fairies to bring you the sweetest fruits from the forest.'

Bottom sighed. 'I'd prefer grass,' he said sleepily, and he shut his eyes. 'But ask your servants not to wake me, please. I'm suddenly feeling very tired.'

He was asleep in moments, breathing loudly. Titania told her fairies to go, kissed Bottom's head, and then put her arms around him. 'Oh, how I love you!' she said dreamily. 'How I love you!' Soon she was asleep too.

Oberon moved quietly towards the bed. Puck, above him in the tree, jumped down to a lower branch.

'Look, Puck,' said Oberon softly, waving his hand at Titania and Bottom. 'Don't they make a pretty pair?'

Puck's face lit up with a mischievous smile as he looked down at the Fairy Queen on her bed.

'I feel sorry for her now,' Oberon said. 'I met her in the forest earlier, and asked for her Indian servant boy. She gave him to me at once, because all she could think about was this hairy-headed fool. Now I've got the boy, I'll undo this hateful magic in her eyes.'

Oberon took out one of the white flowers, and pressed it in his hand, dropping the juice onto Titania's eyes.

'Oh, how I love you!' Titania said dreamily.

Let this flower change your eye,
And make your love for this fool die.

'Now, my Titania, wake up, my sweet Queen,' he said.
At once, Titania sighed and slowly opened her eyes. She
sat up in surprise when she saw Oberon.

'My Oberon!' she said. 'I've had very strange dreams. I
thought I was in love with . . .' She shook her head, then
laughed. 'I thought I was in love with an ass!'

Oberon took her hand. 'There he is,' he said, looking
behind her at Bottom, still sleeping in the wide flowery bed.

Titania jumped up out of the bed. 'How did this
happen?' she cried. 'How can I have been in love with *him*?
That *human* . . . that *animal* . . .'

'Be calm, Titania,' Oberon said. 'Puck, take the ass's
head off this man. When he wakes up, he'll think he's been
dreaming. Titania, tell your servants to give us music –
music that will make these five humans sleep like the dead.'

As Oberon spoke, Puck's black fog began to lift from the
ground below Titania's bed. There, on the grass nearby, lay
the four young lovers: Lysander and Hermia, Demetrius and
Helena. Fairies carried the still sleeping Bottom, now with
his human head, to the ground and laid him on the grass.

Titania called to her servants. At once the sweet sound
of music filled the air.

'Come, my Queen,' said Oberon, taking Titania's
hands in his. 'Let us dance together, around these sleeping
humans. Let us celebrate our love for one another, both
old and new.'

In the starlight, they danced, and above them their fairy
servants danced too, white lights and green lights together
in the dark trees.

'And tomorrow night,' said Oberon, 'we will dance
at Duke Theseus's house. Our fairy dance will bring
happiness to him and his new wife, and to these four young
lovers, whose wedding day it will also be.'

'My fairy King,' called Puck. 'It's nearly morning.'

'Let's go,' said Titania. 'And you can tell me why I was
found here with these humans.'

*As the sun comes up, the fairies leave, following the night as
it moves slowly around the world. Soon Titania's night palace
disappears, and only the five humans are left in that place in
the forest: Bottom, lying among flowers on the ground, and
nearby, the four lovers, deep in sleep . . .*

Bottom was the first to wake, and in his waking dreams
he was still rehearsing *The story of Pyramus and Thisbe.*

'When it's my turn to speak, call me . . .' he said in a
voice thick with sleep. 'I wait until Thisbe says, 'My lovely
Pyramus . . .'

Then he sat up, and looked around him. 'Hey!' he called.
'Peter Quince? Flute? Snout? Starveling? Where are they?
They went away and left me here sleeping, all on me own!'

He scratched his head, remembering his dream.

'Oh, I've had a very strange dream – the strangest dream
any man has ever had. Only a fool would tell anyone about
it. I thought I was . . . And I thought I had . . . well, only a
fool would say what I thought I had. I will get Peter Quince

to write a song about this dream, and I'll call it "Bottom's Dream". Yes – and I'll sing it in front of the Duke!'

Bottom got up and walked away through the forest, full of ideas about the song he would sing for the Duke.

The sun shines in a clear sky, and Theseus and Hippolyta, with Egeus and their servants, ride through the forest, enjoying the summer morning. They come to a clearing, and see four young people lying on the grass, deep in sleep.

'Who is this?' said Theseus, stopping his horse. Egeus rode forward, to look more closely.

'My Lord, this is my daughter,' he said, astonished. 'And that's Lysander . . . and Demetrius, and Helena. What are they doing here?'

'Perhaps they came to celebrate midsummer in the forest,' said Theseus. 'But Egeus, isn't today the day when Hermia has to choose to marry Demetrius, or to go into a convent?'

'It is, my Lord,' said Egeus.

Theseus called to a servant behind him. 'Wake them!' The servant got down from his horse and shook the four young people awake. They stood up, eyes wide with surprise, staring up at the Duke and the other riders.

Theseus turned to Lysander. 'I thought you and Demetrius were enemies. What are you doing here, sleeping next to the man you hate?'

Lysander looked around, astonished. 'My Lord, I'm only half awake . . . I honestly can't tell you how I came here. But I think . . . yes, I'm sure . . . I came here with Hermia. We wanted to run away from Athens. We wanted to . . .'

'That's enough, my Lord!' Egeus shouted, furious. 'He must be punished! They were trying to cheat us, Demetrius. Lysander was trying to steal my daughter, and break my promise – my promise that Hermia should be your wife.'

Demetrius stepped forward, and bowed to the Duke. 'My Lord,' he said. 'Helena told me that Hermia and Lysander had run away to this forest. I followed them here, and Helena followed me.' He shook his head slowly. 'I can't understand how this has happened, but . . . I don't love Hermia any more. My love for Hermia seems like a dream. Now, my only wish is to be with Helena. Before I ever saw Hermia, I was in love with Helena, and now, that love has returned. She is my one true love, and always will be.'

There was a little silence after these surprising words. Then Theseus smiled. 'Well, my friends, it is lucky that you have met us here. We'll hear more about this later.' Theseus turned his horse and spoke to Egeus behind him. 'Egeus, I am going to go against your wishes. These lovers will be married, at the same time as myself and Hippolyta. We will go back to Athens, the six of us, and begin our celebrations. Come, Hippolyta.'

The two pairs of lovers took each other's hands, and Hippolyta, smiling, reached out and took Theseus's hand too. Then she and Theseus turned and rode their horses away through the forest, followed by Egeus and the servants.

When they had gone, the four lovers looked at each other, all thinking the same thing. What had happened last night?

'Are we dreaming?' said Demetrius. 'Was the Duke really here, and did he really tell us to go with him?'

'*She is my one true love, and always will be.*'

'Yes,' said Hermia. 'He was here, and so was my father.'

'And Hippolyta,' Helena said.

'And the Duke told us to go with him to be married,' said Lysander.

'Well, we're awake then!' Demetrius laughed. 'Come on then, and let's talk about what happened while we walk.'

And so there are three weddings – the Duke marries his love Hippolyta, Lysander marries Hermia, and Demetrius marries Helena. It is a happy day in Athens, and the Athenian people celebrate – but not in Peter Quince's house. Quince, Flute, and Snout are sitting at a table, with long, worried faces.

The door opened, and Starveling came in. At once the others jumped up.

'Have you been to Bottom's house?' Peter Quince said. 'Has he come home yet?'

'No one knows where he is,' replied Starveling. 'He's been taken away, I'm sure he has. Turned into an ass and taken away!'

'We can't do the play without him,' said Flute.

'No,' said Quince, shaking his head slowly. 'It'd be impossible. There's not a man in Athens who could play Pyramus like him.'

Flute sighed. 'He's the cleverest workman in Athens, Bottom is.'

'So fine-looking, too,' said Quince. 'And oh, he has a sweet voice!'

Snug came in from the street, taking off his hat. 'The wedding's finished, and the Duke and his new Duchess are on their way back to the palace now – and not just them, but there were four more lords and ladies married today as well! Just think of the money we could make from our play! Oh, why did Bottom have to go and disappear like that!'

The door suddenly flew open, and in came Bottom, his ass's head gone, smiling from ear to ear.

'Where are my boys?' he laughed.

'Bottom!' the actors cried, jumping up and throwing their arms around him. For a while everyone was talking at once.

'I have the most wonderful and the most extraordinary things to tell you!' said Bottom. He was quiet for a moment, thinking. 'But I won't say a word.'

'Go on, Bottom!' his friends cried, and Bottom looked around at them importantly.

'All right, I'll tell you everything.'

The men waited, but there was silence.

'Tell us, Bottom!' called Quince.

Bottom looked around the room, his eyes shining. 'All I will tell you is this: the Duke has had his dinner. So get your costumes ready, put on your beards, tie up your shoes, and look at your words . . . Because the people at the palace want to see our play!'

CHAPTER 8

The play in the palace

In the great hall in Theseus's palace, Hippolyta and Theseus and the wedding guests take their seats around a stage. The wedding dinner is over, and it is time for everyone to enjoy themselves . . .

'It was so strange,' Hippolyta said to her new husband, 'what those young lovers were talking about at dinner.'

'Strange, but probably not true,' said Theseus. 'Lovers always have their heads full of funny ideas.'

'Yes, but when they talked about what happened last night, they all remembered the same things,' Hippolyta said. 'It did all seem quite extraordinary.'

The new husbands and wives entered the hall – Lysander with his Hermia, and Demetrius with his Helena. They took their seats next to Theseus and Hippolyta.

'Here you are,' said Theseus. 'My friends, I wish you every happiness in your lives together.'

'And we wish the same to you, my Lord,' said Lysander.

'Now then,' the Duke said, 'what is there to entertain us before bedtime? Shall we have music, or dancing, or a play?

Theseus's servant came forward, bowed, and handed him

a paper. 'My Lord, there are three plays to choose from.'

Theseus took the paper and read it. 'A play about a battle, one about the death of learning . . . No, no, these are not suitable for an evening of wedding celebrations. Ah, what's this one?' He smiled. '*The long and short story of young Pyramus and his love Thisbe, a sad and funny play.*' He turned to Hippolyta, laughing. 'Long and short? Sad and funny? What will this be like – hot ice?'

'My Lord,' said the servant, 'It is short, but still much too long. And it is only funny because it is so badly acted. The actors are a group of Athenian workmen – men who work with their hands, and know nothing at all about putting on a suitable play for your wedding day.'

'And we will see it,' said Theseus. 'If these workmen have worked hard to make a play for us, then that is enough for me. We should watch them, and enjoy.'

Hippolyta looked at Theseus. 'I don't like making fun of poor workmen,' she said.

'Listen, my sweet,' he said. 'It is kinder to watch them. In that way we give them thanks for their hard work.'

The servant called the actors, and the audience got ready to watch. First, there was the prologue. It was the strangest of prologues – with all the full stops in the wrong places.

Peter Quince enters as Prologue. Music plays, and when it stops, he begins to speak.

PROLOGUE: We have come here today, not wanting to.
   Offend we hope very much that we will.
   Not upset you, this is not our wish.

Our true hope is.

To please you, we have not come.

To terrify you, we will now show you the sad but funny story of Pyramus and Thisbe.

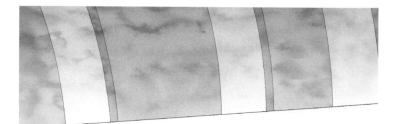

'*He ends his sentences in all the wrong places!*' *Theseus said.*

Theseus looked at the others. 'He ends his sentences in all the wrong places!' he said.

'Yes,' said Lysander. 'He says he doesn't want to terrify or offend us, but his full stops tell us the opposite!'

'He's like a child playing music,' said Hippolyta. 'A learner, with a lot to learn.'

The actors come on – Bottom as Pyramus, Flute as Thisbe, Snout as Wall, Starveling as Moonshine, and Snug as Lion. They bow, and Peter Quince continues.

PROLOGUE: My lords and ladies, our brave lovers, Pyramus and Thisbe, agree to meet by moonshine at Castle gate. Thisbe arrives first, but the Lion comes and frightens her away, you see, and she drops her coat, and the Lion picks the coat up in his bloody mouth, and then brave Pyramus comes, and finds his lovely Thisbe's coat, all with blood on it, you see, and so Pyramus thinks Thisbe is dead, and he pulls out his brave sword and bravely stabs himself and falls down. And Thisbe comes back and finds him and bravely takes his sword and bravely dies. And they and Lion and Moonshine and Wall will tell you all the rest.

Everyone except Wall leaves the stage.

Theseus smiled. 'I wonder if the lion is going to speak,' he said to Demetrius.

'I wouldn't be surprised,' laughed Demetrius. 'Look, the wall is going to say something.'

Wall steps forward, holding a large stone under his arm. Then he holds his other hand up, and makes a circle with his finger and thumb.

WALL: My name is Snout, and I am here to play a wall. This stone I am carrying shows you that I am a wall, and my finger and thumb, you see, make the hole in the wall through which these poor lovers Pyramus and Thisbe whisper to each other.

'What a wonderfully helpful wall!' Theseus whispered.

'It's the cleverest wall that I've ever heard, my Lord,' Demetrius laughed. 'But look – here comes Pyramus.'

Pyramus walks onto the stage, and Wall quickly puts out his arm, to make the hole in the wall with his finger and thumb. But Pyramus is not looking at him and walks into his hand, banging his nose. Pyramus shakes his head, steps back, and Wall lowers his arm.

PYRAMUS: Oh Wall, where is my dear Thisbe? Has she forgotten her promise to meet me here? Oh Wall, oh sweet and lovely Wall, show me your hole.

Wall holds up his finger and thumb to make a circle.

Oh, thank you, Wall. How kind you are! But wait, I can't see Thisbe through the hole. Where is my love? Oh Wall, oh cruel and hateful Wall, I hate your empty hole!

'I think the wall should reply to Pyramus,' said Theseus, laughing, 'and call him bad names too.'

On the stage Bottom turned to speak to the Duke. 'Oh

no, my Lord, he shouldn't do that. You see, the words *empty hole* tell Thisbe to come on stage, and then I talk to her through the hole. Look – you see! She's coming on now.'

Thisbe comes on, and speaks in a little high voice.

> THISBE: Oh Wall, I wish you were not always between me and my lovely Pyramus.
>
> PYRAMUS: I hear a voice. Oh Thisbe, is that you?
>
> THISBE: Oh my love, my own true love!

'I hear a voice. Oh Thisbe, is that you?'

PYRAMUS: Thisbe, kiss me through the hole of this cruel Wall!

THISBE: But I kiss the Wall's hole, not your lips!

PYRAMUS: Then meet me now at Castle gate, my Thisbe.

THISBE: Oh my love, I will run to Castle gate at once.

Pyramus and Thisbe leave the stage.

WALL: The wall has finished now and is not needed again, so I go away, you see.

Wall leaves the stage. Moonshine and Lion come on. Lion looks out at the audience through the lion's neck.

LION: Dear ladies, who have gentle hearts, you will shake with fear when Lion roars, so I'm here to say don't be afraid because I'm just a man and my name is Snug.

'What a gentle, kind lion!' said Theseus.

'Ssh!' said Hippolyta. 'Let's listen to the moon.'

Moonshine steps forward and holds up his lantern.

MOONSHINE: This lantern is the moon, and I am the man in the moon. That's all I have to say.

'He should get inside the lantern,' said Theseus. 'He can't be the man in the moon unless he is inside it.'

'He is afraid of being burned,' laughed Demetrius. 'Ah, but here comes Thisbe, looking for her Pyramus.'

Thisbe enters, looking afraid.

THISBE: This is Castle gate. Where is my love?

Lion jumps at Thisbe and gives a gentle roar. Thisbe drops her coat, and runs screaming from the stage.

'Well roared, Lion!' said Demetrius.

'Well run, Thisbe!' laughed Theseus.

'Well shone, Moon!' said Hippolyta. 'And now comes Pyramus.'

Pyramus walks towards Moonshine, and stops to pick up Thisbe's coat from the ground. He sees that it is covered in something red, and falls to his knees.

PYRAMUS: What terrible thing has happened here? My dear, my love, your coat's all covered in blood! Oh hateful Lion, that has taken my love from me! She is – no, no, was – the loveliest lady that I ever saw. Come night! Come death! Come sword, and do your work!

He takes out his sword and pretends to stab himself.

Now I am dead, and my spirit flies away. Go away, Moon, I must die now – die, die, die, die, die.

Moonshine leaves the stage, and Pyramus lies down and dies noisily.

'With a doctor's help, he'll get better,' Theseus said.

'But why has Moonshine gone before Thisbe comes back to find her lover?' asked Hippolyta.

'She will find him by starlight,' said Theseus. 'Here she comes, and then that will be the end.'

Thisbe comes back onto the stage, sees Pyramus lying dead, and runs towards him.

THISBE: Oh Pyramus, are you dead? Speak, speak! Open those sweet eyes! What, no word, no breath, all gone?

Oh come night! Come death! Come sword, and do your
work! And so goodbye, goodbye, goodbye!
Thisbe pretends to stab herself with Pyramus's sword.

'So now they are both dead – and only Moonshine and
Lion are left,' laughed Theseus.

'Yes, and Wall too,' said Demetrius.

Bottom sat up on the stage. 'No, they pulled the wall
down,' he said. 'Would you like to hear our epilogue now?'

'No epilogue, please,' laughed Theseus. 'Thank you
for your play – we will none of us forget it!' He turned to
Hippolyta, and the other newly-weds. 'Lovers, we must go
to bed. We have two weeks of celebrations ahead of us.'

Talking and laughing, the wedding guests began to leave
the great hall. Soon they were on their way back to their
homes, under a starlit sky.

*It is midnight, and when the last guest has gone from the
palace room, a green light dances in through the window. It
is fairy-time now, and Puck is the first to arrive at the Duke's
house. Soon he is followed by Oberon and Titania, with their
fairies, who sing and dance to bring happiness to the Duke
and his new wife, and the other young newly-weds. They go
quietly through the palace, filling each room with soft and
peaceful fairy music. But by morning the spirits of the night
are gone, and everything is quiet. Perhaps they too were just
a dream.*

GLOSSARY

ass a donkey – an animal like a horse, with long ears

astonished very surprised

audience the people who watch something together (e.g. a play)

bow (*v*) to move the top half of your body forwards and down (when meeting an important person)

breath air that you take in and out through your mouth or nose

celebrate (*v*) to do something special for an important day or other reason; **celebration** (*n*)

clearing (*n*) an open place in a forest where there are no trees

convent a place where religious women called nuns live

costume the clothes worn by actors in a play or film

cruel unkind

duchess the wife of a duke

duke one of the most important men in a country

entertain to interest and amuse somebody

epilogue at the end of a book, play or film, something that is said or written about what has happened

exhausted very tired

fairy a small person in stories who can do magic

fog (*n*) a kind of thick cloud just above the ground; **foggy** (*adj*)

fool someone who says or does things that are not intelligent

fun / make fun of to laugh at somebody or something unkindly

furious very angry

guest a person that you invite to your home (or a party, etc.)

human a person

jealous wishing you had something that somebody else has

juice the liquid from fruit or vegetables (or, here, a flower)

kiss to touch somebody with your lips to show love

knee the part between the top and bottom of the leg

law rules in a country that say what people can or can't do

lead to go with or in front of somebody to show them the way

lion a kind of cat, which is large, yellow, and dangerous

lord (**my Lord**) a name used when talking to people like dukes

magic making impossible things happen by saying special words or doing special things

mischievous (*adj*) enjoying doing things that annoy other people; **mischief** (*n*)

newly-wed (*n*) someone who is just married

offend to make someone feel angry or unhappy

press (*v*) to push something hard with your hand

prologue an introduction to a play, book, or film

rehearse to practise something (e.g. a play) before you do it in front of other people

roar to make a loud deep sound

scratch to move your fingers and nails across your skin

servant a person who works in another person's house

sigh to let out a deep breath because you are sad, tired, etc.

spirit a magic character like a fairy; also, the part of a person that is not their body

stab to push a knife or sword into something or somebody

stage the part of a theatre where the actors do their play

sword a very long sharp knife, used for fighting

terrified/terrifying very frightened/frightening

upset (*v*) to make somebody feel unhappy or worried

NON-STANDARD LANGUAGE USED IN THIS STORY

t'other the other

'em them

learnin' learning

not . . . nobody not anybody

on me own on my own

somethin' something

ACTIVITIES

Before Reading

1 Read the introduction on the first page of the book, and the back cover. What do you know now about the story? Choose T (True) or F (False) for each of these sentences.

1 Lysander, Demetrius, Helena, and Hermia have love problems. T / F
2 In the forest they watch the play by the workmen. T / F
3 Something happens to one of the workmen which makes his friends very frightened. T / F
4 The Athenians cannot see the fairies in the forest. T / F
5 This is a funny story about love and magic. T / F

2 What can you guess about this story? Choose endings for these sentences (you can choose more than one).

1 In *A Midsummer Night's Dream* . . .
a) people fall in and out of love very quickly.
b) a fairy gives one of the lovers a donkey's head.
c) the Duke of Athens gets married.
d) the four young Athenians fall asleep in the forest.

2 At the end of the story . . .
a) there are three weddings and a play.
b) someone dies.
c) everyone goes back to Athens.
d) the workmen make a lot of money.

ACTIVITIES

While Reading

Read chapters 1 to 3. Use the list of names to complete the sentences about the people in the story.

Bottom, Demetrius, Egeus, Flute, Helena, Hermia, Hippolyta, Lysander, Oberon, Puck, Quince, Snug, Theseus, Titania

_____ is the Duke of Athens, and he and _____ are getting ready for their wedding day. _____ is angry with his daughter _____ because she will not marry _____. She is in love with _____, and together they decide to run away from Athens. They tell _____ about their plan.

At a house in Athens, five men listen as _____ tells them about a play they are going to act in. _____ is playing Pyramus, _____ is playing Thisbe, and _____ is the lion.

The king of the fairies, _____, has had an argument with his wife _____, and he decides to make trouble for her. He wants his mischievous fairy _____ to help him.

Before you read chapters 4 and 5, can you guess what the magic juice will do?

1 It will make Titania fall in love with . . .
    a) Puck   b) Nick Bottom   c) Theseus
2 It will make Lysander fall in love with . . .
    a) Titania   b) Helena   c) Hippolyta

Read chapters 4 to 6, and then answer the questions.

1 Who woke up and found herself alone in the forest?
2 Who fell in love with Helena?
3 Who was given an ass's head?
4 Who went away into the forest to fight?
5 Who put magic juice in Lysander's eyes?

Before you read chapter 7, can you guess what happens?
Circle Y (Yes) or N (No).

1 Hermia goes to a convent and nobody gets married. Y / N
2 Lysander marries Hermia. Y / N
3 Demetrius marries Hermia. Y / N
4 Demetrius marries Helena. Y / N
5 Bottom finds his friends and they do their play. Y / N

Read chapter 8. Here is Helena, telling one of her friends about the play. Complete her speech with these words.

deaths / frighten / funny / hole / lion / moon / wall / workmen

'In the evening a group of _____ acted the play of *Pyramus and Thisbe*. It was very strange! One actor was a _____, and his finger and thumb made a _____ through which the lovers spoke to each other. Another actor was the man in the _____, and then there was a _____, a very kind, gentle animal. He said he didn't want to _____ us, and he was only a man called Snug. The play ended with the _____ of Pyramus and Thisbe. We all tried not to laugh, but it was really very _____.'

ACTIVITIES

After Reading

1 Perhaps this is what some of the characters in the story are
thinking. Which six characters are they, and who or what are
they thinking about? What is happening in the story at the
moment?

1 'Where are they? They can't just run away! I'll find them
here somewhere, and then Hermia will have to marry me.'

2 'She still refuses to give me that boy, so I'll make some trouble
for her! Now let's see what happens when she wakes up!'

3 'Where is he? Someone has taken him! Someone has killed
him! He would never leave me like this! I know he wouldn't.'

4 'Silly fool! Now this will give your friends a surprise. What
will happen when they see your face? Let's see!'

5 'I hear his voice, but when I follow, he's gone. Where is lovely
Helena, I wonder? Safe from that little cat Hermia, I hope.
Why did I ever love her? I'm exhausted – I think I'll sleep
here for a while.'

6 'What a success! Listen to them all talking about it! They
loved it! And when I found Thisbe's coat, and stabbed
myself – that was the best part of the whole play, I really
think it was.'

2 **Use the clues to complete this crossword with words from the story. (All the words go down.)**

1 An animal like a donkey.

2 *Pyramus and Thisbe* is a _____.

3 Oberon thought that Demetrius was _____ to Helena.

4 The part played by Snout.

5 Puck was one.

6 The part played by Snug.

7 The colour of the magic flower.

8 The law in Athens says a daughter must _____ her father.

9 Oberon knew a flower that had a magic _____.

10 Lysander and Demetrius wanted to fight with these.

11 The workmen met to _____ their play for the Duke.

12 Someone who is not intelligent.

13 Pyramus and Thisbe spoke through a _____ in the wall.

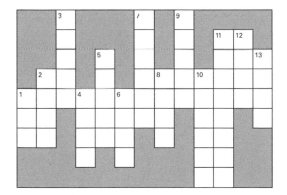

Now find the hidden sentence of four words, reading across.

1 What is the sentence?   3 What was he talking about?

2 Who said this?   4 Was he right?

3 Here is Bottom talking to Quince, Demetrius talking to a friend, and Oberon talking to Titania. **Write in the speakers' names, and then put the sentences in the right order to make a passage of four sentences for each speaker.**

1 _____ 'Helena followed me, and I was so cruel to her, running away and leaving her alone.'

2 _____ 'But when I saw you with him, I felt sorry for you, and I undid the hateful magic.'

3 _____ 'I was angry with you, so while you were sleeping, I put juice from a magic flower into your eyes.'

4 _____ 'Suddenly this beautiful fairy woman appears and says she loves me! She takes me through the forest to her palace and puts flowers around my head.'

5 _____ 'Helena told me that Hermia and Lysander had run away to the forest, and I went after them.'

6 _____ 'Let me tell you about my very strange dream.'

7 _____ 'Then sometime in the night, I realized it was not Hermia that I loved – it was Helena!'

8 _____ 'Next thing I know, I wake up in the forest, and you and the others have all gone!'

9 _____ 'The magic made you fall in love with the first thing you saw, which was that workman with an ass's head.'

10 _____ 'Then, while I lie on her bed, she tells her fairy servants to scratch my head, and bring me food.'

11 _____ 'And now we will be friends again for the wedding tomorrow night.'

12 _____ 'So in the end Lysander married Hermia, and Helena and I were married the same day!'

4 In the prologue to *Pyramus and Thisbe*, Quince 'ends his sentences in all the wrong places'. Rewrite the prologue, beginning and ending the sentences in the right places.

We have come here today, not wanting to. Offend we hope very much that we will. Not upset you, this is not our wish. Our true hope is. To please you, we have not come. To terrify you, we will now show you the sad but funny story of Pyramus and Thisbe.

5 This is a story about fairies and magical things. What do you think about fairies?

1 Do you believe in fairies?
2 Do you know anybody who believes in fairies?
3 Does anybody believe in fairies in today's modern world?
4 How many stories do you know about fairies, or similar spirits, in your own culture?
5 Are they stories about spirits who help people, or spirits who make trouble, like Puck?
6 What do you think a fairy looks like?

6 Imagine that, like Oberon, you know a magic flower. The juice of it, dropped into people's eyes, can change the way they see things. Think about these questions.

1 Whose eye would you like to drop the juice into?
2 How would you want to change what they see? (Imagine that the juice can change anything – not just who the person is in love with.)

ABOUT THE AUTHOR

William Shakespeare (1564 –1616) was born in Stratford-upon-Avon, a small town in central England. His father was a glove-maker, and a businessman who bought and sold things. His mother was Mary Arden, the daughter of a landowner. Little is known about Shakespeare's early life. He went to school in Stratford, and at eighteen he married a local girl called Anne Hathaway, with whom he had three children. His wife and children stayed in Stratford, but by 1592 Shakespeare was living in London, writing plays and also working as an actor. In 1594 he joined a company of actors called The Lord Chamberlain's Men, and began to write more and more plays. In 1595 he wrote *Romeo and Juliet*, his famous play about love and families at war. In 1599 The Lord Chamberlain's Men built a theatre called The Globe, where many of Shakespeare's plays were performed. The company also took the plays to court, and acted them before Queen Elizabeth I, and after her death, King James I.

By the time he was in his late forties, Shakespeare was successful and rich, buying houses and land in London and Stratford. He began to spend more time in Stratford with his family, only going to London for business or rehearsals of a new play. He died in Stratford on his birthday in 1616, when he was only fifty-two years old. You can read more about the events and people in his life in a story in the Oxford Bookworms Library, *William Shakespeare* (at Stage 2).

Shakespeare wrote more than thirty plays, and *A Midsummer Night's Dream* is one of the most popular. It was written in the 1590s, and has been performed on stages around the world, and also made into ballets, operas, and films.

What a strange play *A Midsummer Night's Dream* is, in so many ways! At the very beginning, Theseus tells us that in four days there will be a new moon – but the following nights are both dark and moonlit. The workmen are told who they will be in their play *Pyramus and Thisbe*, but some of the parts they are given never appear. And the fairies are so small they can sleep in nutshells, but their queen Titania can put her arms around Nick Bottom, a fully grown man. The play is full of impossible problems like these – but because it is so magical, none of them seem to matter.

So what is the most important part of *A Midsummer Night's Dream*? Even after 400 years, people are still arguing about it. Some people think that the workmen/actors who perform the *Pyramus and Thisbe* play show Shakespeare at his cleverest and funniest. Some people think that the fairies are the most important thing in the play, because they control what happens to everyone else. Other people believe very strongly that the love story of the four young Athenians is the heart of *A Midsummer Night's Dream*. The best thing is to go and see the play in a theatre or watch a film of it, and decide for yourself!

OXFORD BOOKWORMS LIBRARY

Classics • Crime & Mystery • Factfiles • Fantasy & Horror
Human Interest • Playscripts • Thriller & Adventure
True Stories • World Stories

The OXFORD BOOKWORMS LIBRARY provides enjoyable reading in English, with a wide range of classic and modern fiction, non-fiction, and plays. It includes original and adapted texts in seven carefully graded language stages, which take learners from beginner to advanced level. An overview is given on the next pages.

All Stage 1 titles are available as audio recordings, as well as over eighty other titles from Starter to Stage 6. All Starters and many titles at Stages 1 to 4 are specially recommended for younger learners. Every Bookworm is illustrated, and Starters and Factfiles have full-colour illustrations.

The OXFORD BOOKWORMS LIBRARY also offers extensive support. Each book contains an introduction to the story, notes about the author, a glossary, and activities. Additional resources include tests and worksheets, and answers for these and for the activities in the books. There is advice on running a class library, using audio recordings, and the many ways of using Oxford Bookworms in reading programmes. Resource materials are available on the website <www.oup.com/elt/gradedreaders>.

The *Oxford Bookworms Collection* is a series for advanced learners. It consists of volumes of short stories by well-known authors, both classic and modern. Texts are not abridged or adapted in any way, but carefully selected to be accessible to the advanced student.

You can find details and a full list of titles in the *Oxford Bookworms Library Catalogue* and *Oxford English Language Teaching Catalogues*, and on the website <www.oup.com/elt/gradedreaders>.

THE OXFORD BOOKWORMS LIBRARY
GRADING AND SAMPLE EXTRACTS

STARTER • 250 HEADWORDS

present simple – present continuous – imperative –
can/cannot, must – going to (future) – simple gerunds …

Her phone is ringing – but where is it?
Sally gets out of bed and looks in her bag. No phone.
She looks under the bed. No phone. Then she looks
behind the door. There is her phone. Sally picks up her
phone and answers it. *Sally's Phone*

STAGE 1 • 400 HEADWORDS

… past simple – coordination with *and*, *but*, or –
subordination with *before*, *after*, *when*, *because*, *so* …

I knew him in Persia. He was a famous builder and I
worked with him there. For a time I was his friend, but
not for long. When he came to Paris, I came after him –
I wanted to watch him. He was a very clever, very
dangerous man. *The Phantom of the Opera*

STAGE 2 • 700 HEADWORDS

… present perfect – *will* (future) – (*don't*) *have to*, *must not*, *could* –
comparison of adjectives – simple *if* clauses – past continuous –
tag questions – *ask/tell* + infinitive …

While I was writing these words in my diary, I decided
what to do. I must try to escape. I shall try to get down
the wall outside. The window is high above the ground,
but I have to try. I shall take some of the gold with me – if
I escape, perhaps it will be helpful later. *Dracula*

STAGE 3 • 1000 HEADWORDS

… should, may – present perfect continuous – *used to* – past perfect –
causative – relative clauses – indirect statements *…*

Of course, it was most important that no one should see
Colin, Mary, or Dickon entering the secret garden. So Colin
gave orders to the gardeners that they must all keep away
from that part of the garden in future. *The Secret Garden*

STAGE 4 • 1400 HEADWORDS

*… past perfect continuous – passive (simple forms) –
would conditional clauses – indirect questions –
relatives with *where/when* – gerunds after prepositions/phrases …

I was glad. Now Hyde could not show his face to the world
again. If he did, every honest man in London would be
proud to report him to the police. *Dr Jekyll and Mr Hyde*

STAGE 5 • 1800 HEADWORDS

*… future continuous – future perfect –
passive (modals, continuous forms) –
would have conditional clauses – modals + perfect infinitive …

If he had spoken Estella's name, I would have hit him. I was
so angry with him, and so depressed about my future, that I
could not eat the breakfast. Instead I went straight to the old
house. *Great Expectations*

STAGE 6 • 2500 HEADWORDS

*… passive (infinitives, gerunds) – advanced modal meanings –
clauses of concession, condition

When I stepped up to the piano, I was confident. It was as if
I knew that the prodigy side of me really did exist. And when I
started to play, I was so caught up in how lovely I looked that I
didn't worry how I would sound. *The Joy Luck Club*